The Joy of Claude Debussy

Compiled by Denes Agay.

Claude Debussy (1862-1918), founder and foremost representative of Impressionism in music is one of the few modern masters whose unquestionable greatness is readily accepted by 20th Century critical consensus. His works, still within tonal boundaries, revolutionized the old rules of harmony with a fascinating array of new devices: whole-tone chords, chord clusters, novel harmonic sequences. His liberating role made possible the new directions of much contemporary music and was one of the strongest influences on the evolution of many of its styles.

For the art of Debussy the piano is the perfect vehicle. His works for this instrument constitute perhaps the most unique and important body of literature since Chopin, occupying a permanent and indispensible place in the repertory.

This volume contains some of Debussy's best-loved and technically most accessible works, including the *complete* Children's Corner set, this deservedly popular modern classic. The volume, as a whole, presents a fascinating compendium of impressionistic tone-painting, lyricism, and humor; unquestionably a joy to perform and listen to.

Denes Agay

This book © 1984 Yorktown Music Press, Inc.
All Rights Reserved

Order No. YK 21269
U.S. ISBN 0-8256-8029-8

Exclusive Distributors:
Music Sales Corporation
24 East 22nd Street, New York, N.Y. 10010 USA
Music Sales Limited
78 Newman Street, London W1P 3LA, England
Music Sales Pty. Limited
27 Clarendon Street, Artarmon, Sydney, NSW 2064, Australia

Printed in the United States of America by
Hamilton Printing Company
1/84

Yorktown Music Press
London/New York/Sydney

Doctor Gradus ad Parnassum

Children's Corner

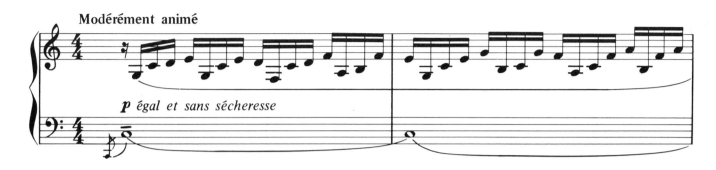

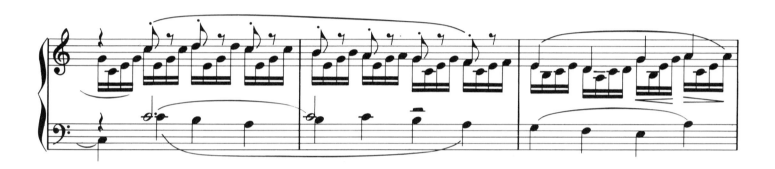

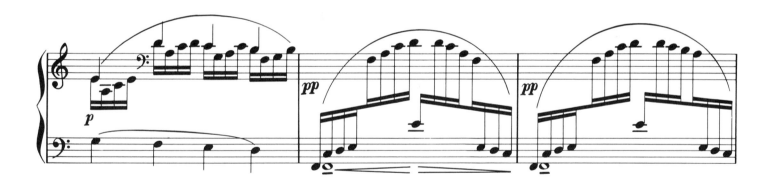

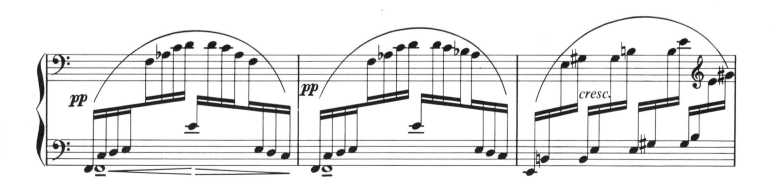

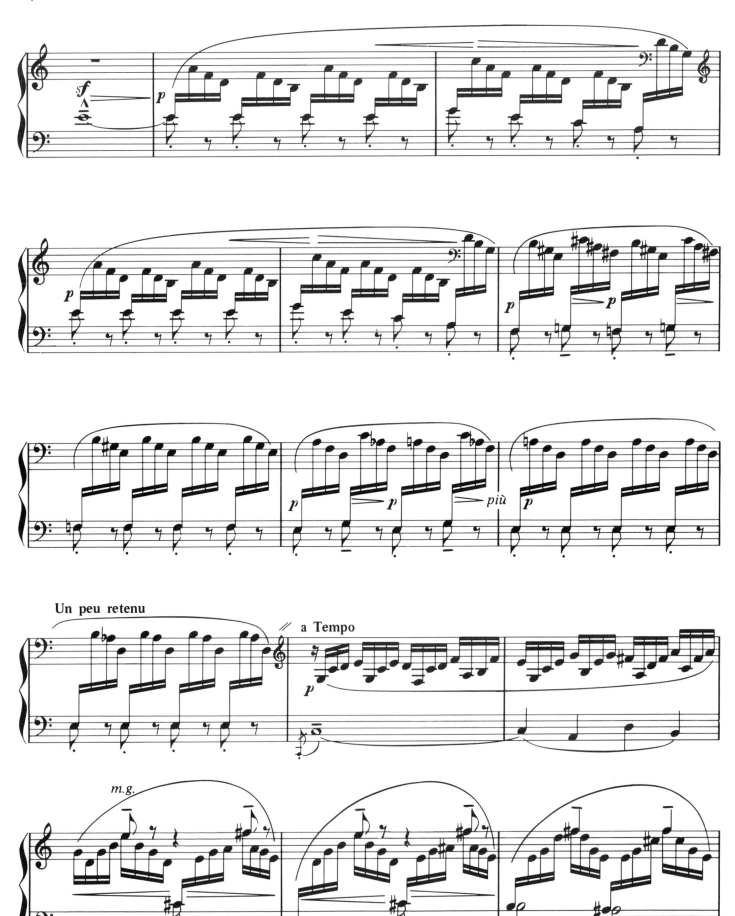

Jimbo's Lullaby

Children's Corner

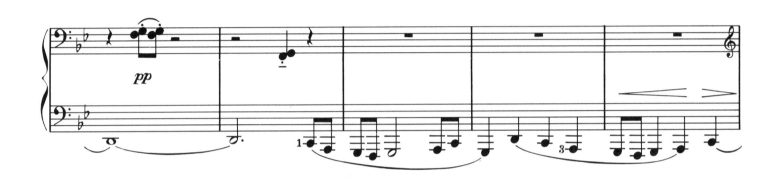

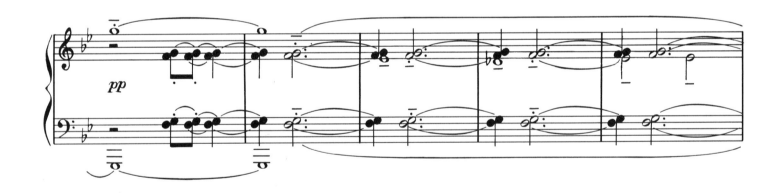

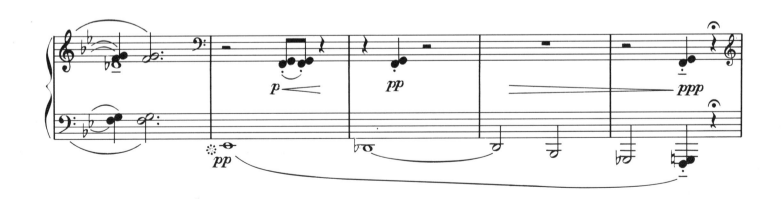

Serenade of the Doll

Children's Corner

The Snow is Dancing

Children's Corner

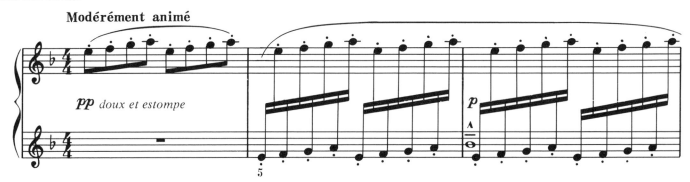

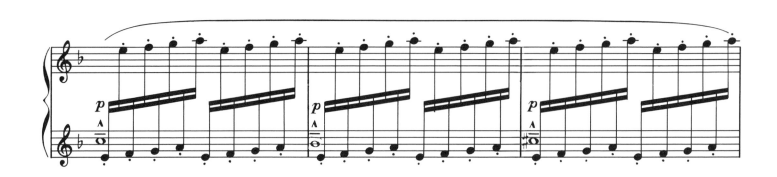

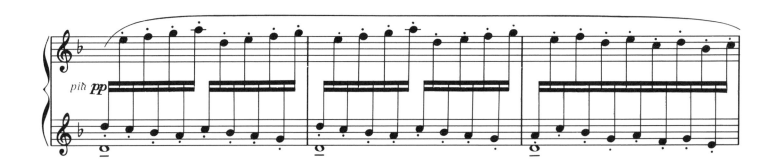

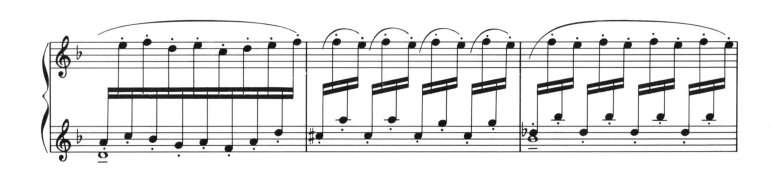

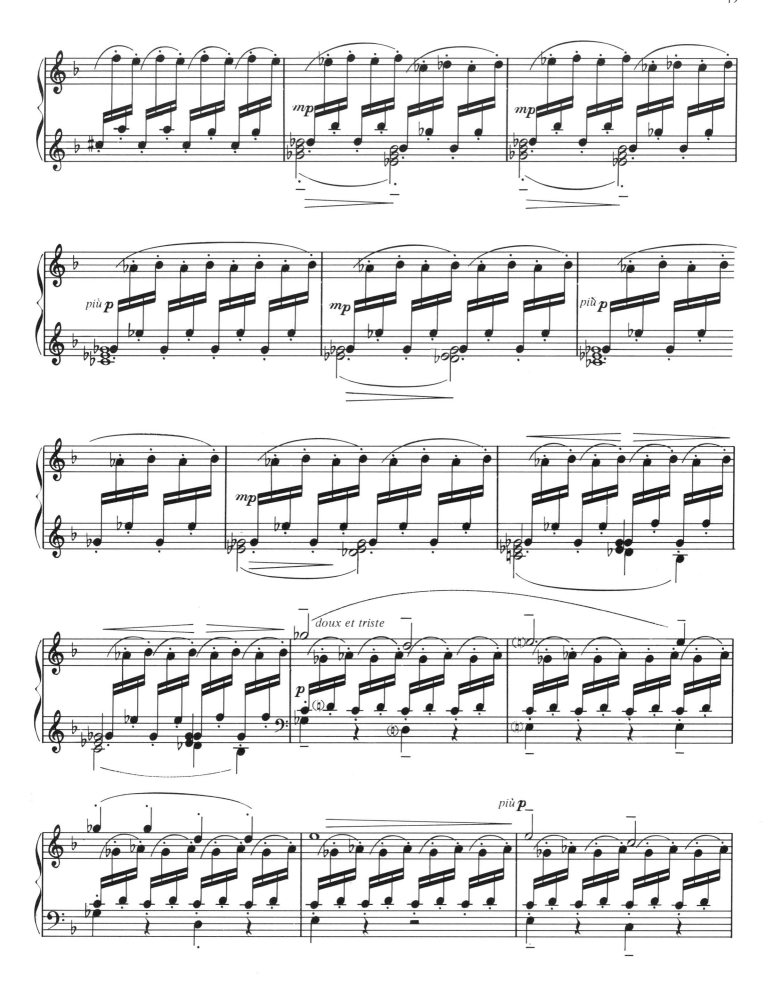

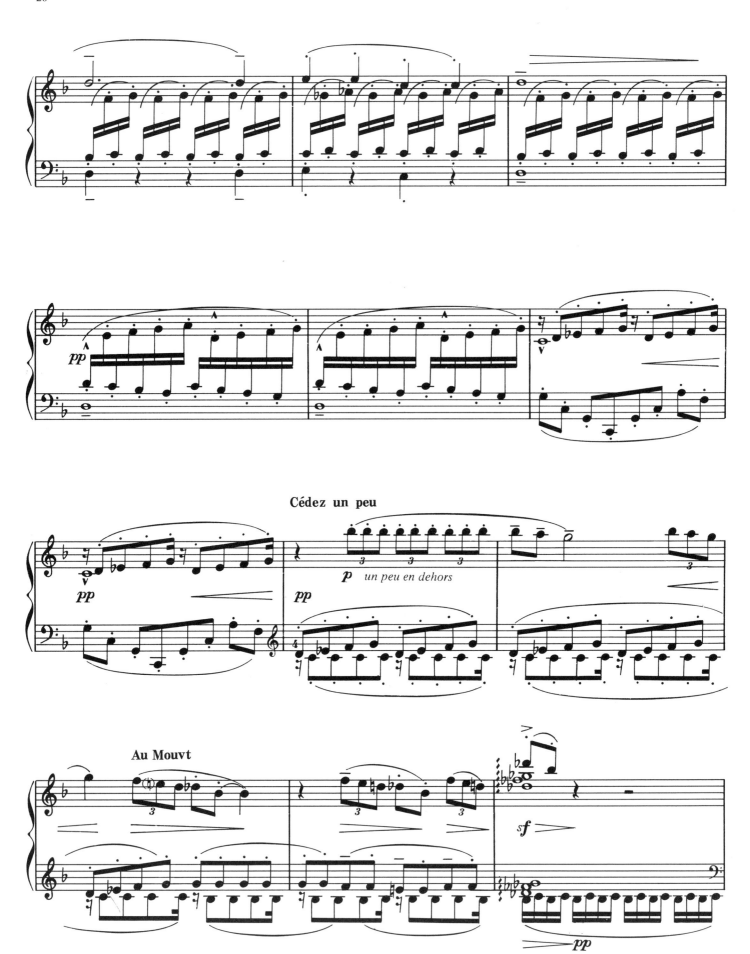

Cédez un peu

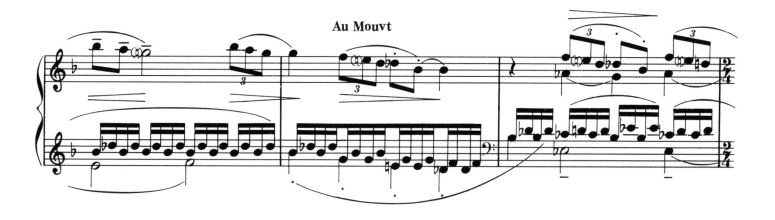

Au Mouvt

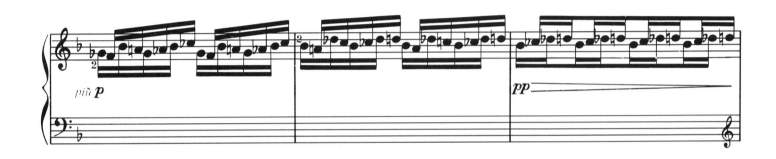

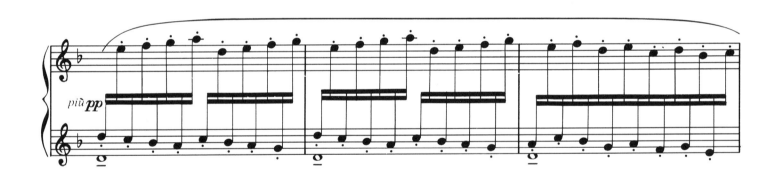

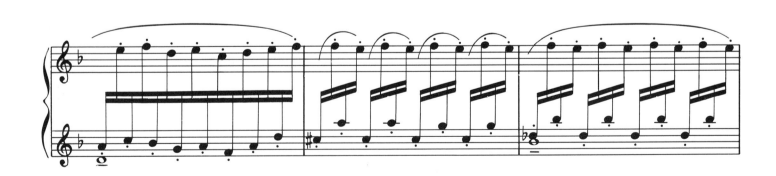

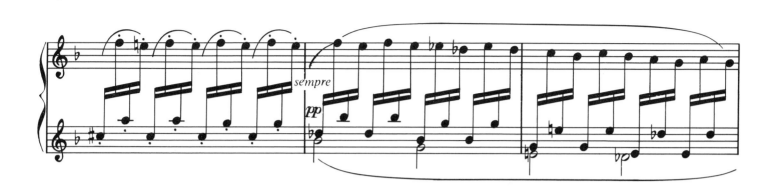

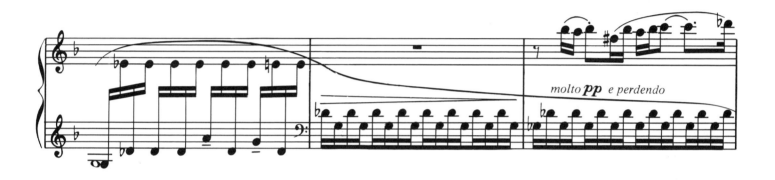

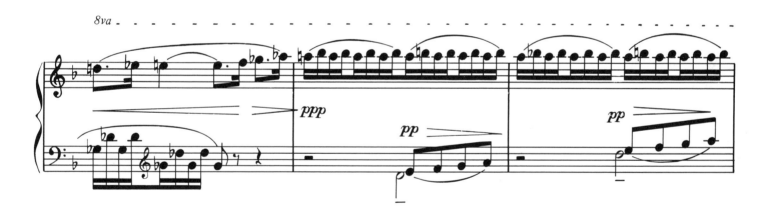

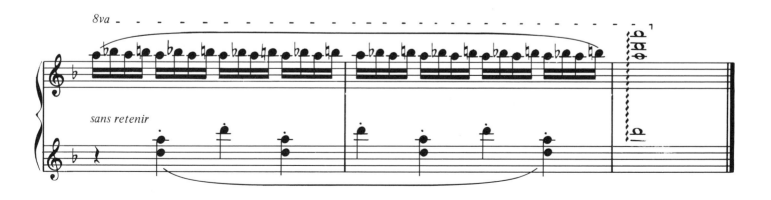

The Little Shepherd

Children's Corner

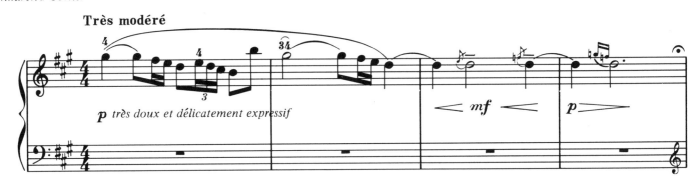

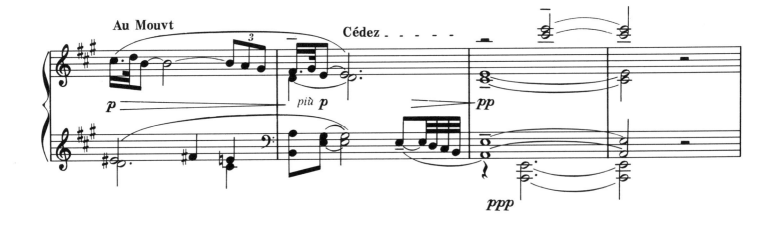

Golliwog's Cake-walk

Children's Corner

28

First Arabesque

Second Arabesque

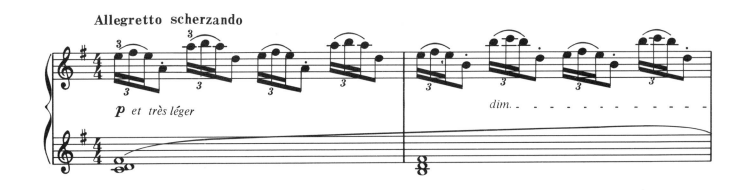

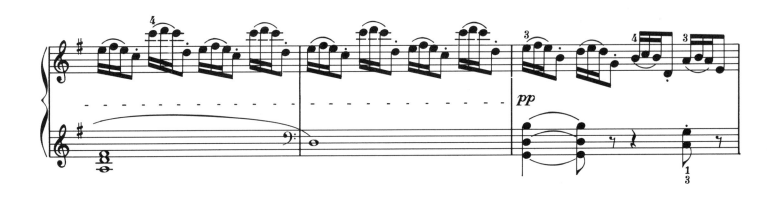

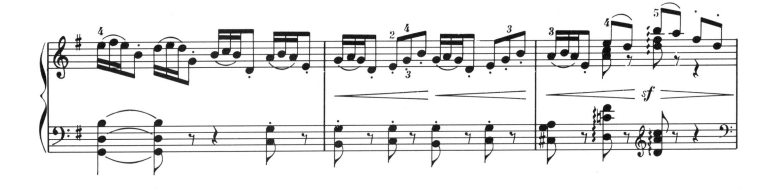

Album Leaf
(1916)

Prelude

Suite Bergamasque

Clair de Lune

Suite Bergamasque

55

pp morendo jusquà la fin

Passepied

Suite Bergamasque

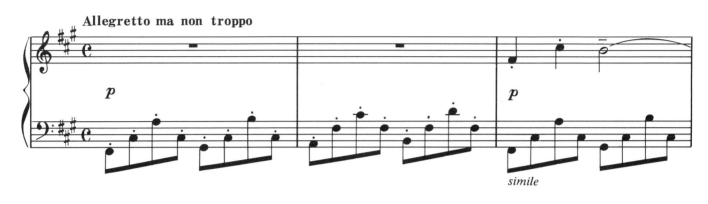

Toccata

Pour le Piano

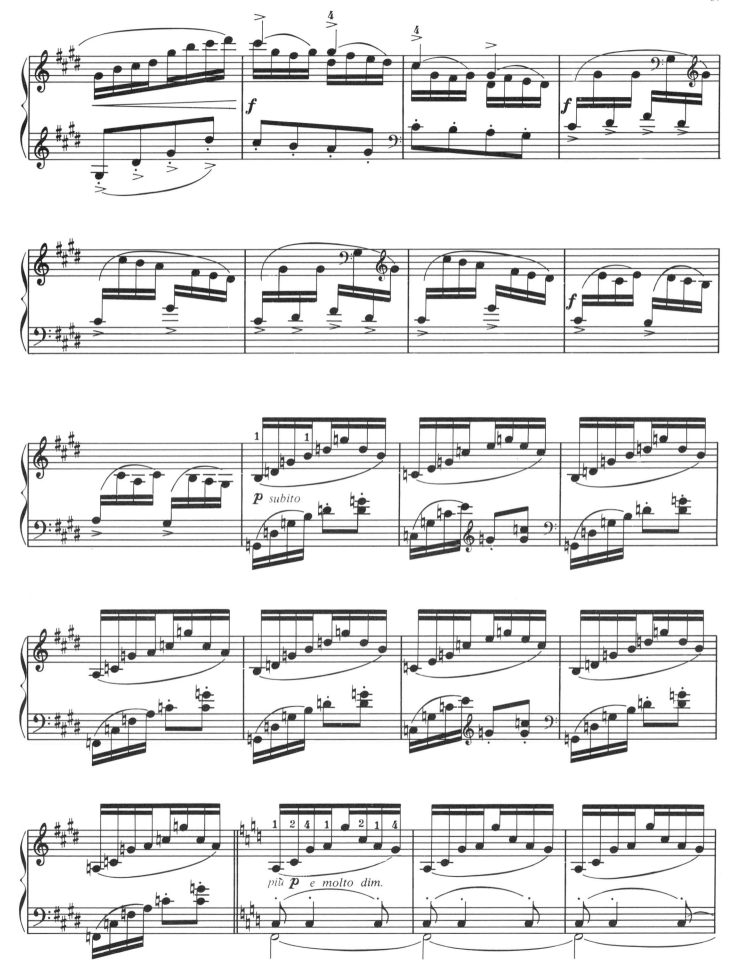

très léger

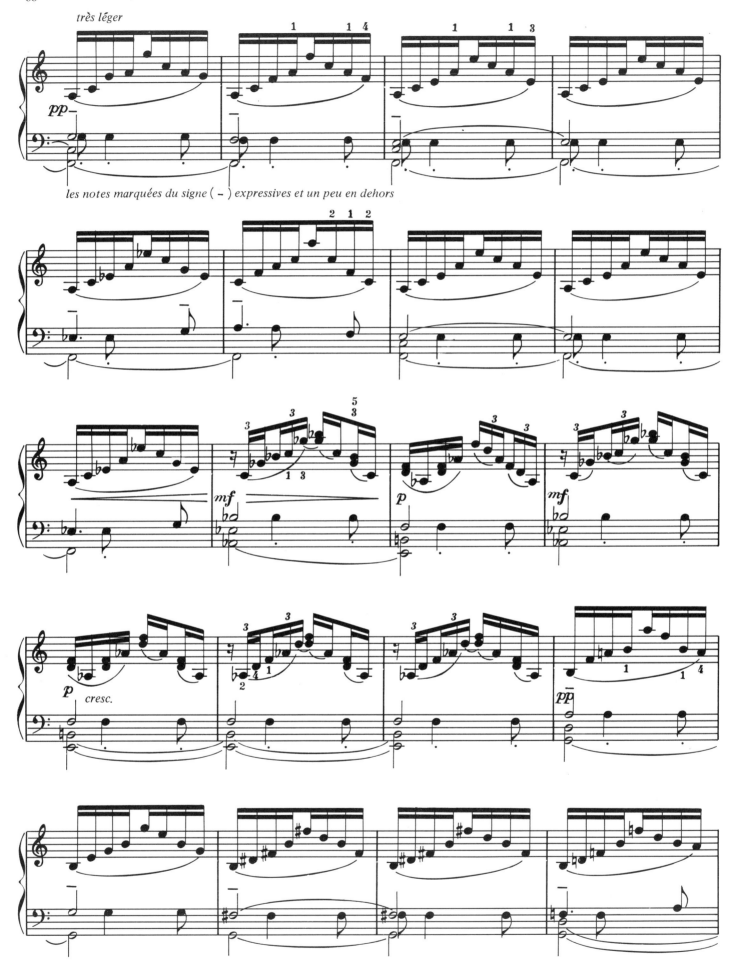

les notes marquées du signe (–) *expressives et un peu en dehors*

à Madame E. Rouart (née Y. Lerolle)

Sarabande

Pour le Piano